THE KIDS ARE ALL RIGHT

THE KIDS ARE ALL RIGHT

Compiled by Tony Husband

Foreword by Michael Palin

SPHERE BOOKS LIMITED

First published in Great Britain by Sphere Books Ltd 1986
27 Wrights Lane, London W8 5TZ

Reprinted 1986

Printed and bound in Great Britain by
Collins, Glasgow

ACKNOWLEDGEMENTS

To: Lady Kathleen Grade, Carole Husband, Sheena Boyd,
Bill Moores, Simon Bond, Ernest Lee Printers, Jim Davidson,
Patrick Moore, Jimmy Cricket, Douglas Adams,
Pete Townshend, Victoria Wood

dedicated to the NSPCC

THE SERIOUS BIT
by Michael Palin

Come on! Don't pretend to be grown up. We're all children at heart, even my Granny and Mr Watkinson, the Bank Manager, who still reads *Beano* inside his copy of the *Financial Times.*

This book is for the child in all of us. A celebration by *Punch* and *Private Eye* cartoonists, and household names like Alexei Sayle and Bob Monkhouse, of what children are all about.

But none of us knows more about children than the NSPCC, and it's to help their work in looking after them that everyone in this book has given something free.

A word of warning. This book is *funny.* It should not be read whilst balancing a plateful of gravy on your sister's head or whilst half-way across the Grand Canyon on a tightrope. It may also make the reader gurgle, splutter, cough and spit out peas uncontrollably. If it doesn't, you're not a child any more, and should go and see your doctor immediately . . . and be sure to take him a copy.

Remember – every good laugh helps the NSPCC help children.

Michael Palin

P.S. My Granny says she didn't find this bit very funny at all.

THE KIDS ARE ALL RIGHT

I'M TRINIDAD, HE'S ENGLAND – WANNA BE THE BLONDE EX-BEAUTY QUEEN?

. . . NOW, WHO'S GOING TO BE THE NSPCC INSPECTOR?

WE'VE CALLED HIM VESUVIUS BUT IT MAY BE JUST WISHFUL THINKING.

DANCING THE NIGHT AWAY.

IT'S A BEAUTIFUL CASTLE, DEAR, AND I'M SURE THE TUNNEL IS VERY, VERY DEEP!

ON BEHALF OF ELSPETH AND MYSELF, I WOULD LIKE TO THANK YOU FOR A VERY SMOOTH CROSSING.

HE'S GOT HIS MOTHER'S EYES AND EARS BUT HIS DADDY'S FUNNY LITTLE WAYS. . .

BAD LUCK REALLY, HE WAS DOING A HEADSPIN AND GOT STUCK IN A POTHOLE!

LUCY........BY DAVE FOLLOWS.

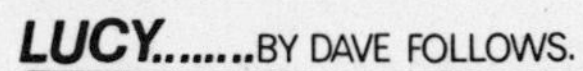

HELLO . . . NSPCC? NOW LOOK HERE, THEY'VE SHUT ME IN MY ROOM AGAIN!

A COLD? YOU HAVE A COLD? MUESLI EVERY MORNING – STONE-GROUND WHOLEWHEAT BREAD – HOME GROWN VEG – IRON TABLETS – AND YOU HAVE A COLD?

WHEN'S PLAYTIME?

. . . DODGER . . . OLIVER. . . THEY'VE ALL GORN, BILL . . . WE WAS RAIDED BY THE NSPCC LAST NIGHT . . .

McLACHLAN

NOW THAT'S WHAT I CALL A CHILD PRODIGY!

BECAUSE RAIN IS WET. BECAUSE THAT'S THE WAY BANANAS GROW. JUST BECAUSE.

IT'S A PITY THEY HADN'T DONE MORE WORK ON THIS KIND OF THING WHILE IT WAS STILL IN THE TEST TUBE!

Wolden

GOAL!

MUM SAID BRING SOME FISH AND CHIPS HOME WITH YOU!
Quanda ©

CRASH!

CAN WE HAVE OUR BALL BACK, MISTER?

Quanda ©

DON'T LET IT DOWN AGAIN. YOUR DAD'S STILL IN INTENSIVE CARE AFTER BLOWING IT UP LAST TIME.

Denis Gifford's
QUICK ON THE DRAW
©R7
BANANA!
RRIIP!
BANANA SPLIT!
Creative Comics©

DAD, WHEN ARE YOU GOING TO TELL ME ALL ABOUT THE FACTS OF LIFE? – UNEMPLOYMENT, DIVORCE, CRIME, DRUGS, STREET VIOLENCE. . .

TELL US AGAIN ABOUT THE OLD DAYS, AND THE RUBIC CUBE.

LOOK AT THIS, A SEX STEREOTYPE'S JOINED THE PLAYGROUP.

I could put him in a private ward for fifty percent of your pocket money!
LITTLE DOCTOR SET
CHIC

OF COURSE YOU CAN'T STAY HOME FROM SCHOOL, I'VE MADE YOUR SANDWICHES.

YOUNG THOMAS IS VERY MUCH LIKE HIS FATHER, ISN'T HE?

IT'S A GOOD LIKENESS – BUT ARE YOUR MOTHER'S SHOES THAT COLOUR?

Alexei Sayle

BLOODY SNOB! CONKERS OUT OF SEASON!

BAD NEWS I'M AFRAID – YOU'VE GOT KIDS!

I THINK WE OUGHT TO TURN IT ORF . . . IT'S FRIGHTENING MUM AND DAD . . .

I THINK WE'RE BEING BUGGED

OH, THAT'S NIGEL – THE CHIEF INSPECTOR'S SON!

MIND YOU, IT'S BROUGHT THE KIDDIES BACK.

HE'S NOT EVEN WARM, IS HE, DAD?

YOU DIDN'T TELL US HOW BIG HE'D GROW WHEN WE GOT HIM.

PLATFORMS
1-10
HONEYSETT

HELLO, KIDS – ANYONE CARE FOR A GAME OF SNAP?

KEVIN
WOODCOCK

THERE'S SOMETHING YOU HAVE TO KNOW – YOU'RE NOT REALLY MY FATHER.

IT ***IS*** THE SCHOOL UNIFORM.

COME BACK, CHILDREN! A BURST TYRE DOESN'T MEAN A DAY OFF SCHOOL.

I HAD NO IDEA THE BEDS SHORTAGE WOULD BE SO ACUTE.

STICK AROUND – LAST WEEK THEY GAVE ME FIFTY PENCE TO GO AWAY.

I DON'T KNOW WHAT COLOUR OF KNICKERS SNOW WHITE WAS WEARING AND, FRANKLY, I DON'T THINK IT'S RELEVANT!

DADDY'S GIRL

DADDY'S GIRL

THE BATTERIES IN MY POCKET CALCULATOR WENT DEAD!

MUM – CALL THE GUINNESS BOOK OF RECORDS – EIGHTEEN OF US IN ONE DUSTBIN!

I MUST ADMIT, SHE'S A DAMN GOOD NIT-NURSE!

ED McHENRY

HE'S GOT HIS FATHER'S BELCH.

RODNEY! – WHERE DID YOU GET THAT CATAPULT ELASTIC FROM?

GRANDAD
OUTFIT

THE MILKMAN LEFT TWO PINTS, A CARTON OF CREAM, HALF A DOZEN EGGS, AND A BABY IN A BASKET, IS THAT RIGHT, DEAR?

ANDY CAPP ©

YOU DON'T POP IN ON US AS MUCH THESE DAYS, JASON –
T176

I DON'T SEEM TO GET THE TIME, UNCLE ANDY, NOW THAT I HELP MY FRIEND WITH HER HOMEWORK

WATCH IT, SON. THE WORLD'S FULL OF BLOKES WHO STARTED OUT HELPING WITH THEIR HOMEWORK – AND ENDED UP DOING THEIR HOUSEWORK
THANKS FOR THE TIP

I WANT A DOLL!

HE'S GETTING TO BE A BIG BOY NOW, ISN'T HE . . .

BONNY BABY CONTEST
THIS DEGRADES BABIES
3rd
1st
2nd
John Witt

ONE DAY, SON, ALL MY LUST, GREED AND ENVY WILL BE YOURS.

WHAT A WEIRD LOOKING KID!
YEH – AND SO BADLY DRAWN!
Bob Monkhouse ...85

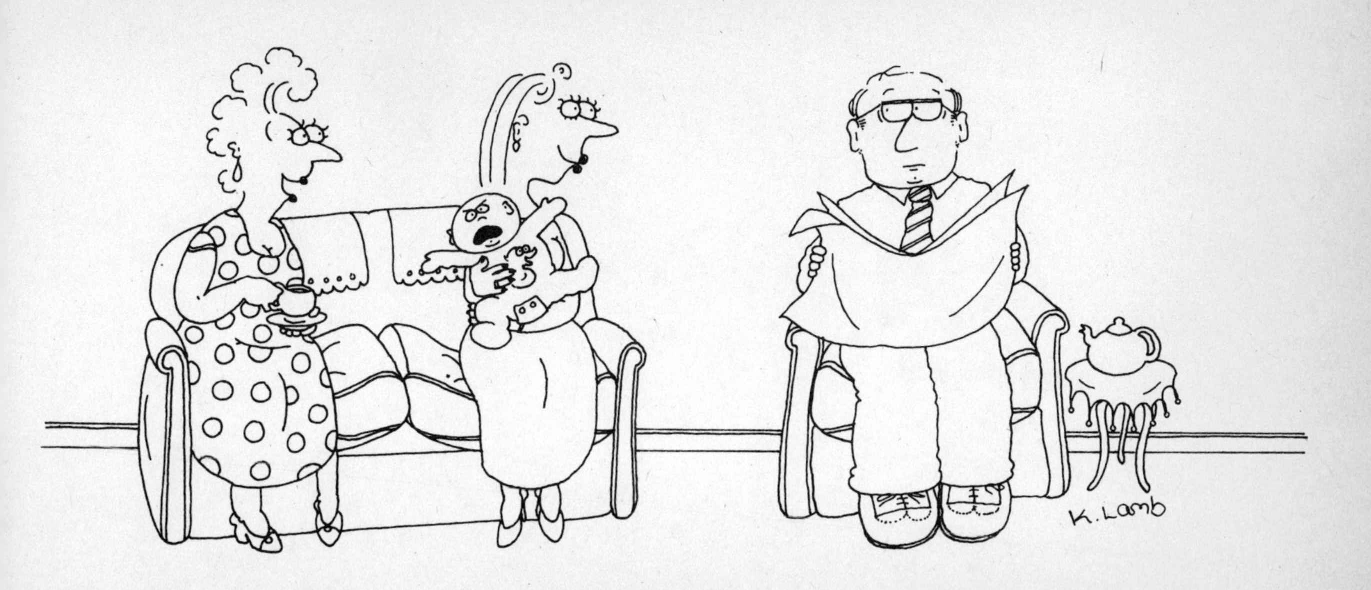

IF HENRY LOST ALL HIS TEETH AND HIS HAIR, HE'D LOOK JUST LIKE BABY!

IT SEEMS TO ME MOTHER JUST DOESN'T APPRECIATE ME AT TIMES!

I MEAN, I KNOW IT'S NOT BRILLIANT BUT....

IT IS ONLY A LOOSE INTERPRITATION OF PICASSO'S SUPERB GUERNICA!
Riley

I'VE ALWAYS WANTED MY PHOTOGRAPH TAKEN... IN THE REPOSE OF SAY....

MICHAELANGELO'S DAVID, OR MAYBE ONE OF HIS VISIONS FROM THE SISTINE..

ANYTHING BUT MUMMY'S LITTLE DIDUMS!
Riley

– ON THE OTHER HAND, DAVID, FROM A CHRISTIAN POINT OF VIEW, MUGGING PEOPLE IN THE STREET IS A CRIMINAL OFFENCE . . .

I REALLY MEANT PUSSYCATS AND BOW-WOWS

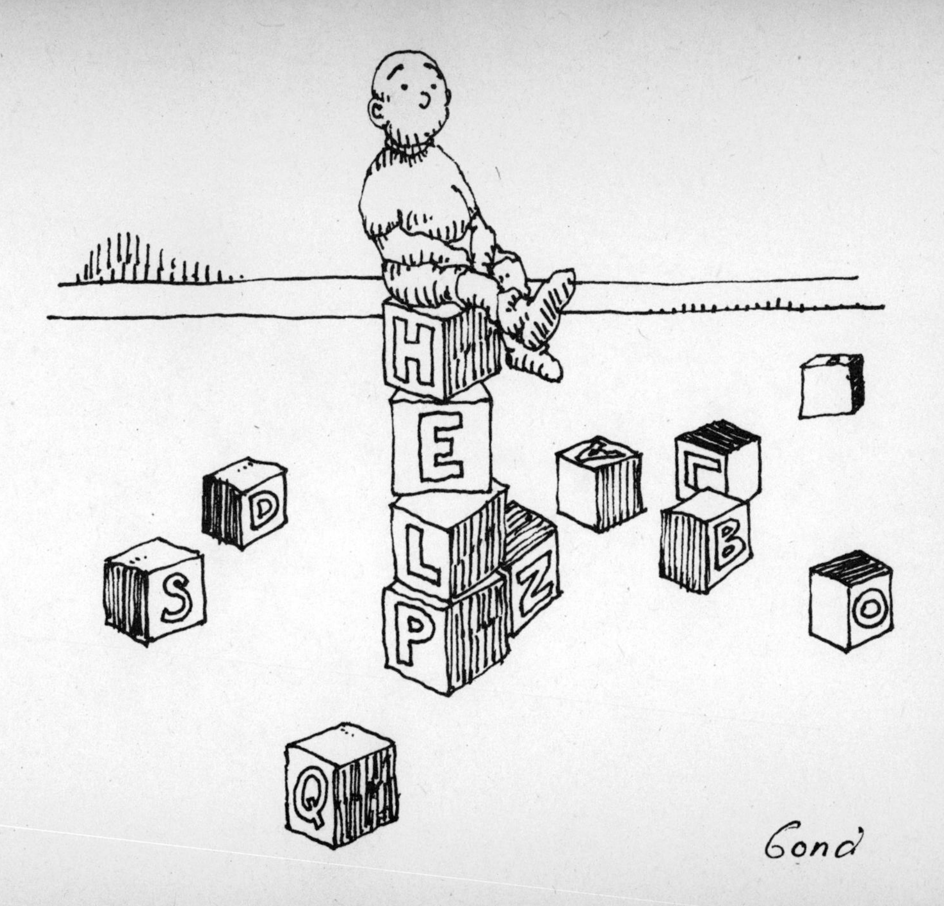
H
E
L
P
Z
D
S
B
O
Q
Gond

SEX EDUCATION IN THE FORTIES

SEX EDUCATION IN THE EIGHTIES

Raymond Briggs

YOU DELIBERATELY CHOPPED THAT WORM IN TWO!

Please Sir - can we do 'DISILLUSIONMENT' for O levels?

Calman

OK, MUGSY, YOU ASKED FOR IT!

small fry by Roy Mitchell

PEANUTS

by Schulz